WHEN'S LATER, DADDY?

Bil Keane

A FAWCETT GOLD MEDAL BOOK
Fawcett Publications, Inc., Greenwich, Connecticut

WHEN'S LATER, DADDY?

A Fawcett Gold Medal Book published by arrangement with
The Register & Tribune Syndicate, Inc.

Printed in Canada

September 1974

"Oh, boy! Can WE play, too, Mommy?"

"I didn't do it. I can scribble better'n that."

"The letter X stands for a kiss, X marks the spot
or a movie we can't see."

"You put the penny in and I'll flush it."

"Sam guesses EVERY TIME which hand I have the dog biscuit in!"

"Telephone, Billy! It's a girl."

"I can wink, see?"

"Of COURSE Grandma likes little boys. But, this time she's invited DOLLY to stay with her for a few days."

"Bye, Mommy! I'll phone when I get there —
if I'm not too busy helping Grandma!"

"I get to sleep in Dolly's room!"
"No! I do, Mommy! Me!"
"I said it first!"

"Gee, Grandma! I didn't know you liked to play with all these things."

"I better not lock the bathroom door, Grandma,
'cause I might lock myself in and you'd have
to climb through the window to get me out."

"Yes, I'm rememberin' my manners...yes, I'm helping Grandma...yes, I'm eatin' all my vegetables...come on, Billy get off the phone and let me talk to Mommy!"

"It's a good thing Billy and Jeffy aren't here 'cause they'd eat up all the cookies. Can I have some more, Grandma?"

"Why do we have to take another nap, Grandma?
I'm not tired."

"Hi, Mommy! This is Dolly. Grandma and I
just had breakfast. Last night we watched
Johnny Carson."

"If Grandpa went to heaven just before I was borned maybe he picked me out for Mommy and Daddy."

"When I grow up, Grandma, I might come and
live with you all the time."

"That's not the kind of peanut butter Mommy
buys. That's not our kind of bread. This is
a different milk. . ."

"Grandma! That lady called you Florence! I
never knew you had a REAL name!"

"...and Mommy gets mad at Daddy when he's
late gettin' home, and Daddy doesn't know
where the money's comin' from to pay all
those bills, and PJ wets the bed, and
Billy kicked the school principal,
and..."

"Don't worry, Grandma, I'll just tell Mommy that we got sick and tired of that pony tail."

"Wait! I'll leave my doll here with you, Grandma, so you won't be too lonely after I'm gone."

"Gracious me! You're all a sight for sore eyes.
Land's sake, Jeffy, how you've grown while
I've been at Grandma's! Doesn't my hair
look SPIFFY? Goodness! I'm famished
for a cup of tea. . . "

"I liked it better bein' an only child at
Grandma's."

"Why does the driver sit on one side of the bus
when she picks Billy up and on the OTHER
side when she brings him home?"

"I would have gotten a hundred if I hadn't missed those six problems."

"Last one in is a
rotten egg!"

"Mommy, Billy called
you a rotten egg!"

"I don't like this kind of bread. It has FRECKLES on it."

"Daddy, lift me up so I can make a basket."

"Hurry up and open it so I can see what
I got you."

"Bite down hard on it with your hind teeth."

"Can't I leave this hair long right here? It's the only way I can grow sideburns."

"Close your eyes and ears. I want to tell
Mommy a secret."

"Mommy said to tell you I had a very nice time."

"I didn't want the skin off my apple. Can you
put it back on for me?"

"Here's a picture of Mommy when she was
building PJ."

"I like that perfume you wear in the morning,
Mommy -- toast and bacon."

"Move over, Daddy -- I can't see."

"Mommy! You said you'd save me the juice cans
so I can make you a pencil holder at school!"

"Pretend you're calling Mommy and Daddy on the phone — that'll make them behave."

"You don't 'spect me to play that do you? It's
for ages three to six -- I'm SEVEN!"

"While you're up there, Daddy, see if you can
find my rocket and frisbee, and Jeff's glider
and Dolly's yellow ball and..."

"I'm NOT laughing!
I'm just SMILING!"

"Mommy, is this a
laugh or a smile?"

"I don't care. That's why I put on lots of perfume -- to keep the boys AWAY from me."

"Now PJ can reach a hand to hold, too!"

"But, I've got my own money to buy it!"

"It's Sam blowing the horn. I guess he wants
us to hurry."

"Do you think God would mind if I killed
this fly?"

"That's for me! I'll get it!"

"Aw, what a gyp! I just PRETENDED I was
takin' a nap and I fell asleep for REAL!"

"Here's a nice bone for Sam if he's being a good
dog and not up on the furniture."

"What ELSE did you see at the zoo
besides flies?"

"And whose little boy are you?"　　"Nonebody's."

"Billy's eating the cookies out of his lunch and
the bus hasn't even come yet!"

"But, Daddy! How does all that snow get
UP there?"

"Mommy! Will you be mad if we tell you somethin'?"

"No, Miss Barbara -- that's not how they taught us to do it on 'Sesame Street'."

"It doesn't have to snow for Santa to get here.
His sleigh rides on air!"

"That Christmas music makes my eyes so happy
they cry."

"I'm not tellin' ANYBODY what I want 'cept
Santa Claus -- not even Mommy!"

"PJ was frowning in this one...Billy moved in
this one, and here Dolly's making a face.
Let's just BUY our cards this year."

"Grandma, did you used to play with Santa Claus when you were a little girl?"

"Every time you open a Christmas card are you
S'POSED to say, 'Did we send them one?'"

"...and then you take this street, and then that street, then this street, and..."

"You know those packages hidden in your closet, Mommy? We didn't find them."

"...and we're also proud of our lovely Karen who is 19 and an honor student again in her sophomore year at Penn. Brad is now a very handsome 17-year-old, 6 feet tall and starring on Central's basketball team. Our summer vacation this year took us first to the beautiful..."

"Look! Joseph is saying the Pledge of Allegiance."

"I guess Santa must have a work shop in Japan,
too, 'cause that's where it says this doll
was made."

"It's Grandma! I'll go open the presents for h..
I mean, the DOOR for her!"

"We're finished playin' with the Christmas toys.
What can we do now?"

"Don't worry, Daddy, I'll clean up all this mess
with the sweeper Santa brought me."

"I just wanted to know if it's New Year's yet so
I could put up my calendar."

"THE BOWL GAMES ARE STARTING!"

"Are you SURE Grandma said to put the money
she gave us in the bank?"

"Can I wear this shirt again? The dirt's in the
back so it won't show."

"Know what Grandma has on her window sill?
A POT OF URANIUM!"

"Know how much I have? I have six moneys!"

"Look! There's a hijacker!"

"I have to get right back outside so all the kids
can enjoy me."

"What time is it when the big hand is on zero
and the little hand is on fourteen?"

"Open the door and let me in!" "Not by the hair of my chinny-chin-chin!"

"We're just bringin' some snow in to play with."

"I'm drawing a cat instead 'cause I can't
spell 'giraffe'."

"I not here -- I with Daddy!"

"Bruce Durack is asking his mother if he can stay here for dinner."

"Mmm! Mommy! I wish you could get a job in there!"

"I sure hope Billy's guardian angel doesn't go on strike."

"How do you like the new glasses Mommy went
out and bought this afternoon?"

"When I die, can I take my blanket with me?"

"That's MY gum you found, Jeffy! And you know the old saying: 'Finders weepers, losers keepers'!"

"Can Lee Bell come over? I don't have anybody to play with."

"You're sitting there looking very cute and
I want you to stop it!"

"Isn't Barfy GOOD, Mommy? He's gettin' rid of all the leftovers for us."

"Remember, Mommy, you only talk to the
teachers about me on PTA nights --
tonight's Open House!"

"Wait! Before you put the goldfish in, I have to
see if this water is the right temp'ture."

"Is it time to feed the goldfish yet?"

"Can I have some of the scraps for the goldfish?"

"There are TEN of us living in this house now --
me, Mommy, Dolly, Jeffy, PJ, Barfy, Sam,
Kittycat, the goldfish...let's see -- that's
nine...Kittycat, the goldfish, and...
oh, yeah -- Daddy!"

"If we don't clean the bowl very often, the water will get diluted."

"Mommy! When I rub my feet on this blanket, there are SPARKS under here!"

"Are most snowmen bald?"

"Instead of just writing 'Billy' on my lunch could you put 'Wild Bill'?"

"Daddy, what's the date of the Fourth of July
this year?"

"Mommy's telling us a Bible story 'bout a
PUNCHY PILOT."

"I got these pants for Easter and nobody EVER
wore them before!"

"I got a hit but somebody caught it before it hit the ground."

"Birds don't sing, they whistle. Right, Mommy?"

"How come you haven't been playing much with the presents we bought you for Mother's Day?"

"I'm going to put this hair of mine away and save it for 'Show and Tell' in college."

"What are these lollipops for, Grandma?"

"Who put the ice cream on the cereal shelf?"

"Mommy, this rose bush BIT me!"

"No, you CAN'T have a penny, PJ! Do you
think money grows on weeds?"

"The can says this lemonade mix makes ONE quart, but we got FOUR quarts out of it!"

"Look! There's a hole in the sky and I can see a
little bit of heaven!"

HAVE FUN WITH THE
FAMILY CIRCUS

WHEN'S LATER, DADDY?	T3078	75¢
HELLO, GRANDMA?	T3103	75¢
THE FAMILY CIRCUS	T3034	75¢
LOOK WHO'S HERE!	T3039	75¢
PEEKABOO! I LOVE YOU!	T3038	75¢
I NEED A HUG	T3106	75¢
WANNA BE SMILED AT?	T3121	75¢
PEACE, MOMMY, PEACE	T3115	75¢
CAN I HAVE A COOKIE?	T3033	75
I'M TAKING A NAP	T3105	75

WHEREVER PAPERBACKS ARE SOLD

If your bookdealer is sold out, send cover price plus 15¢ each for postage and handling to Mail Order Department, Fawcett Publications, Inc., P.O. Box 1014, Greenwich, Connecticut 06830. Please order by number and title. Catalog available on request.